TO ALL CHILDREN WHO HAVE SICKLE CELL AND FELT DIFFERENT BECAUSE OF THE DISEASE, FEEL EMPOWERED. YOU ARE SUPER, EVEN WHEN YOU DON'T FEEL GOOD. EVEN SUPERHEROES NEED BREAKS.

SUPER CELLS

Princess Publishing
Denton, TX

ISBN: 978-0-578-54608-7

Printed in the United States of America
First Edition: September 2019

Cover Design and Illustrations: D.J. Hicks
Interior Layout: D.J. Hicks

SUPER CELLS

BY PRINCESS WALLS

ILLUSTRATED BY D.J. HICKS

DEFEATING THE ODDS

HI, MY NAME IS GIZELLE.

MOMMY SAYS I HAVE SOMETHING CALLED SICKLE CELL AND SOMETIMES MY BLOOD CELLS TURN INTO WEIRD SHAPES, CAUSING MY BODY TO HURT.

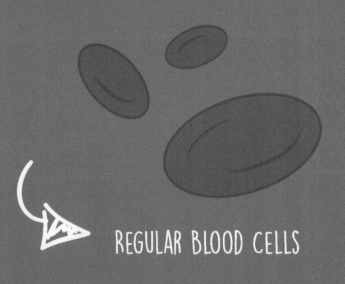

REGULAR BLOOD CELLS

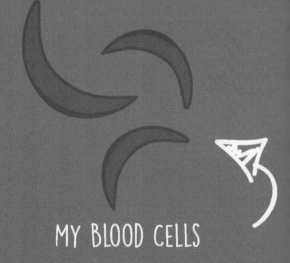

MY BLOOD CELLS

WHEN MY BODY HURTS I CAN'T DO OTHER THINGS, LIKE GO OUTSIDE AND PLAY WITH MY FRIENDS.

WHEN THIS HAPPENS, IT'S TIME FOR ME
TO PUT ON MY CAPE AND BATTLE
THE EVIL SICKLE CELL!

THE PAIN CAN HURT SO BAD THAT SOMETIMES I HAVE TO GO THE HOSPITAL AND GET HELP FROM MY SIDEKICKS. THEY LET ME REST AND FILL MY BODY WITH SPECIAL POWERS!

MY CELLS ARE ALWAYS READY TO
BATTLE BUT I HAVE TO MAKE
SURE I STAY HEALTHY AND
PREPARED AS WELL!

BECAUSE WHEN I DO, I'M ABLE TO GO OUTSIDE AND PLAY WITH MY FRIENDS.

MY CELLS ARE SUPER
AND SO ARE YOURS!!!

CPSIA information can be obtained
at www.ICGtesting.com
Printed in the USA
BVHW020504121121
621380BV00007B/362